THE FASHION DESIGN
Colouring Book

CARLTON BOOKS

CW00765116

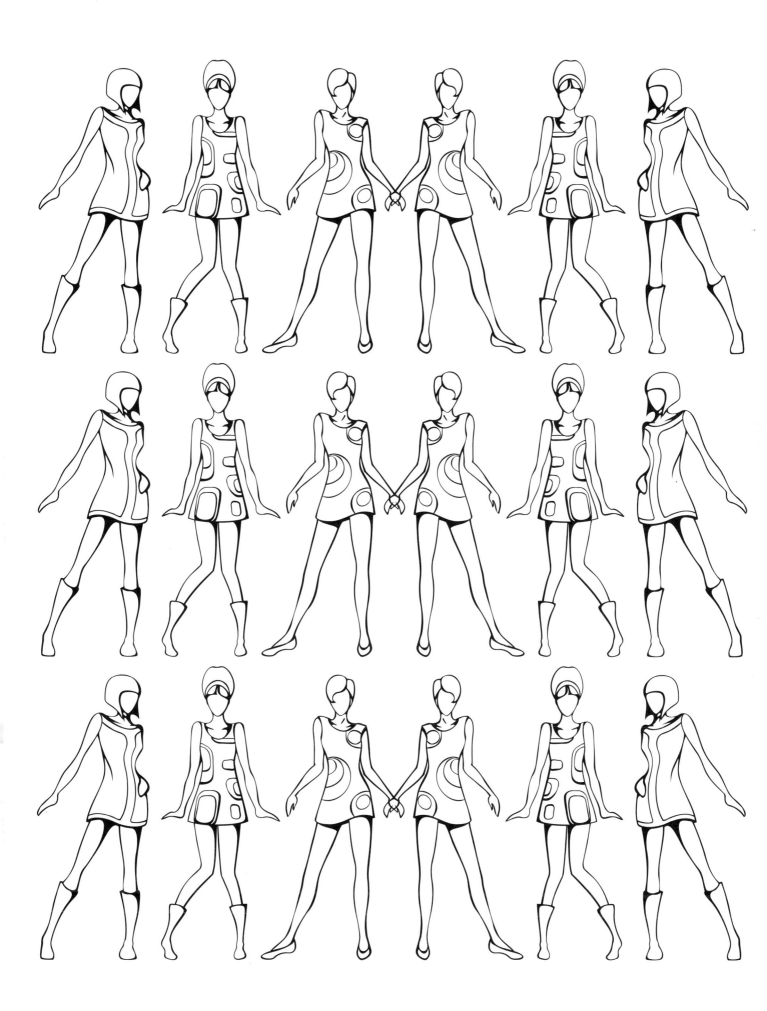

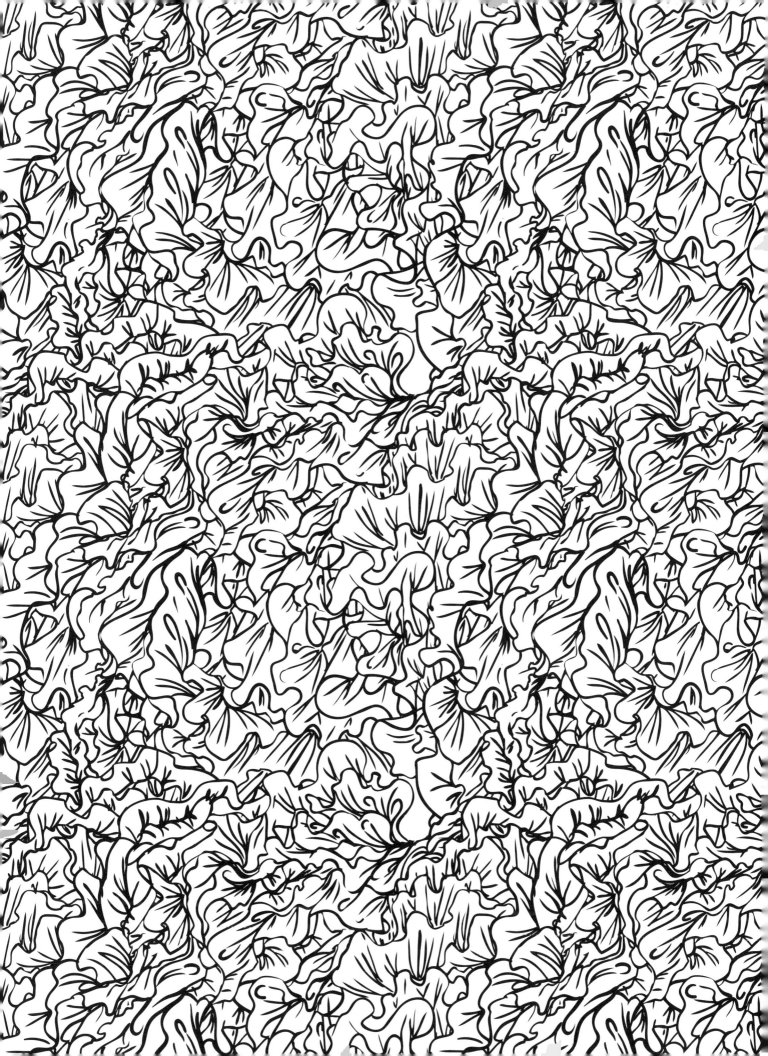

15/Apr/2016
CDatton

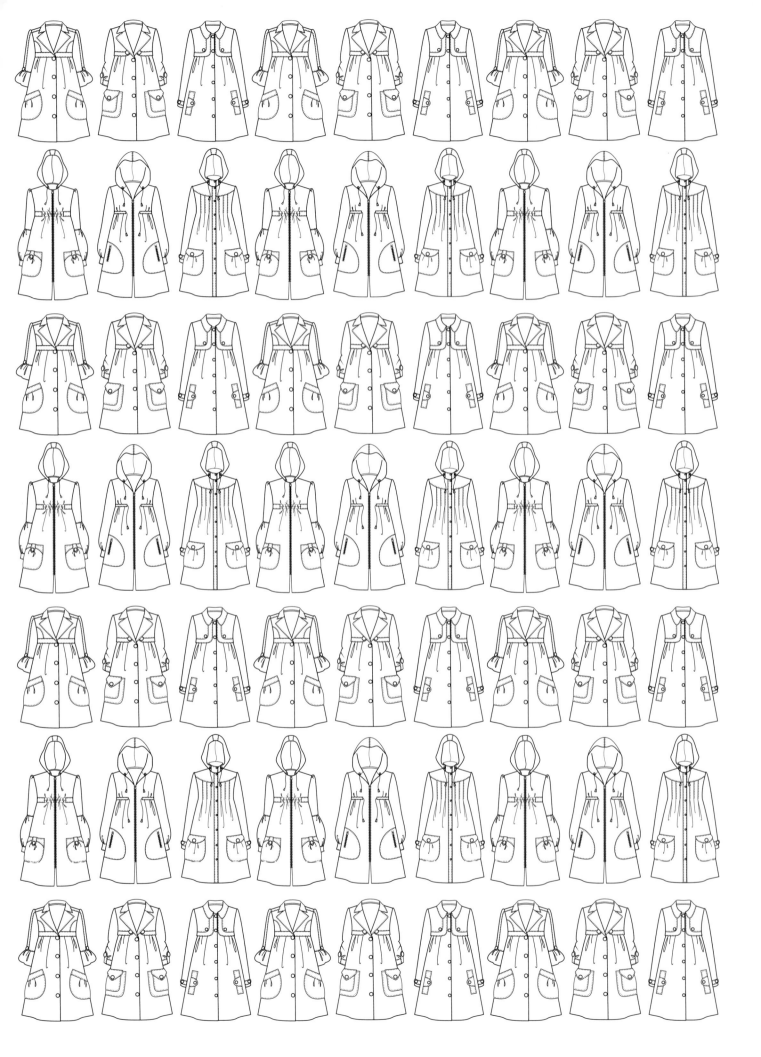

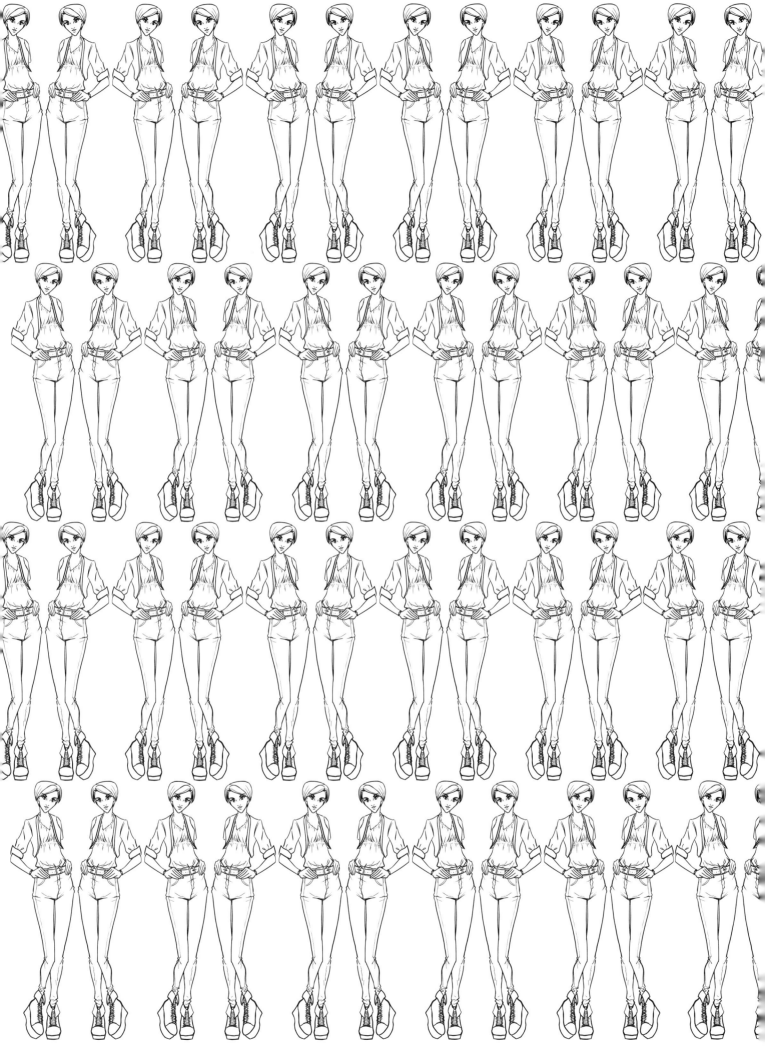

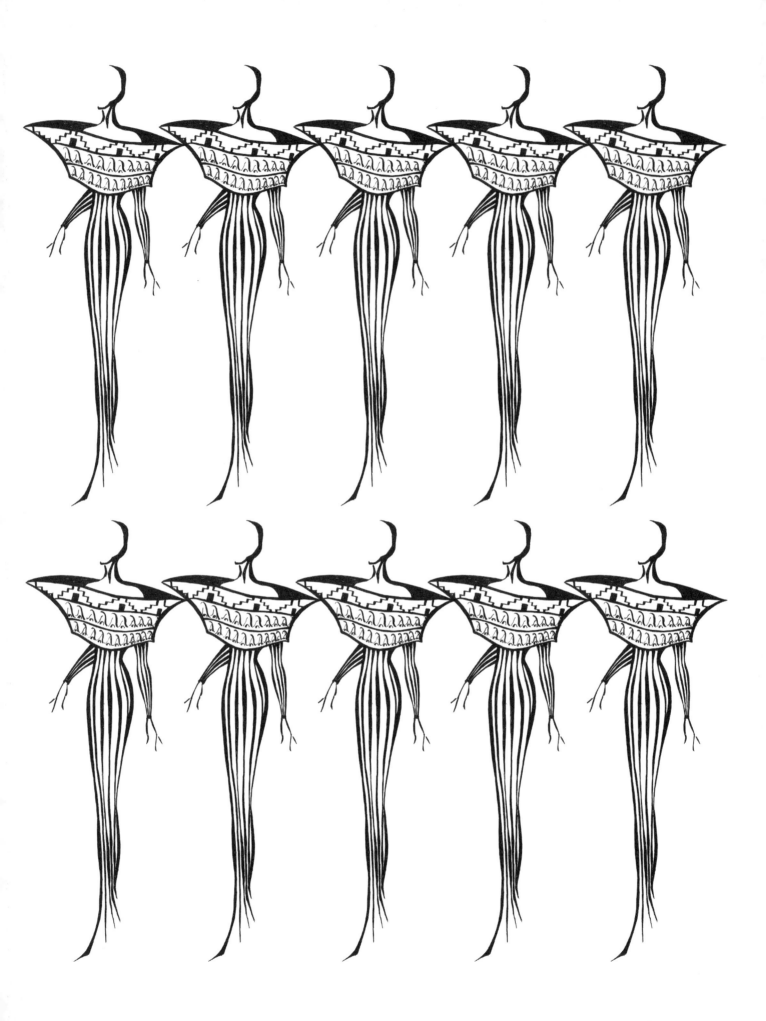

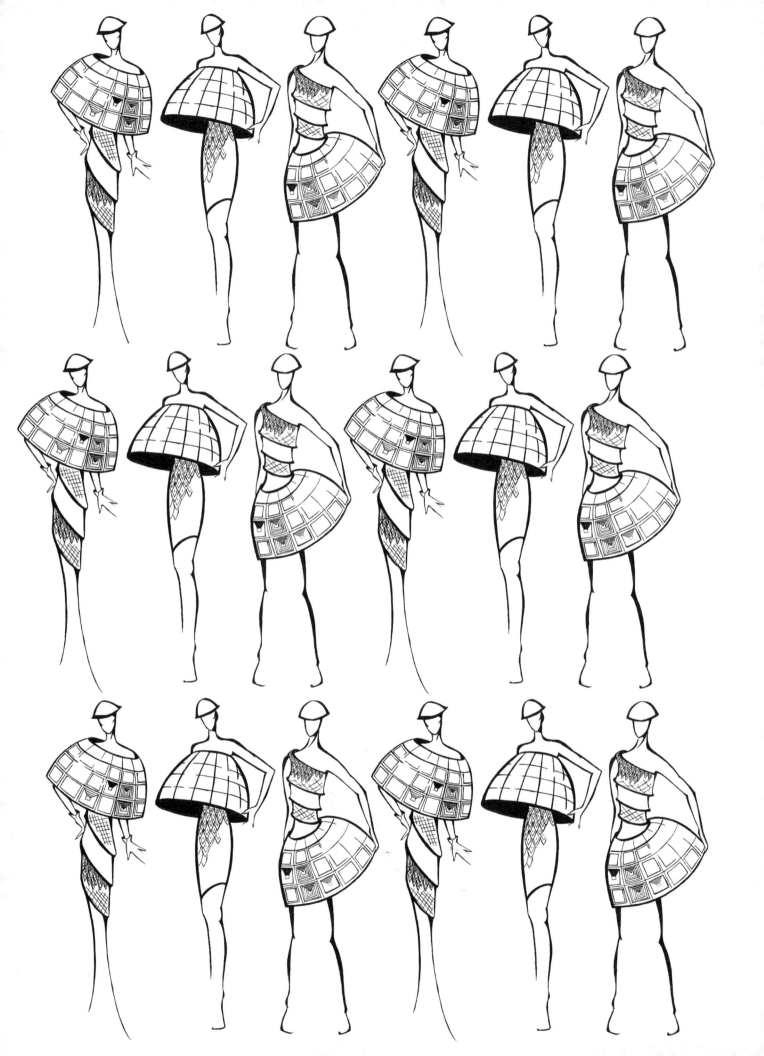

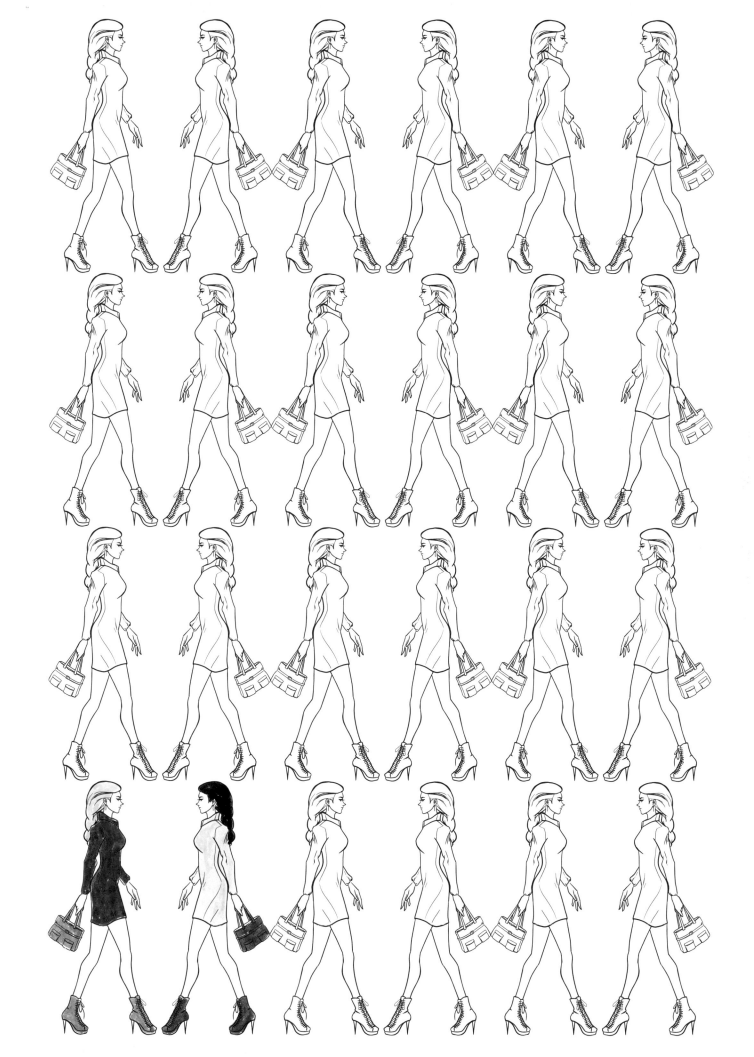

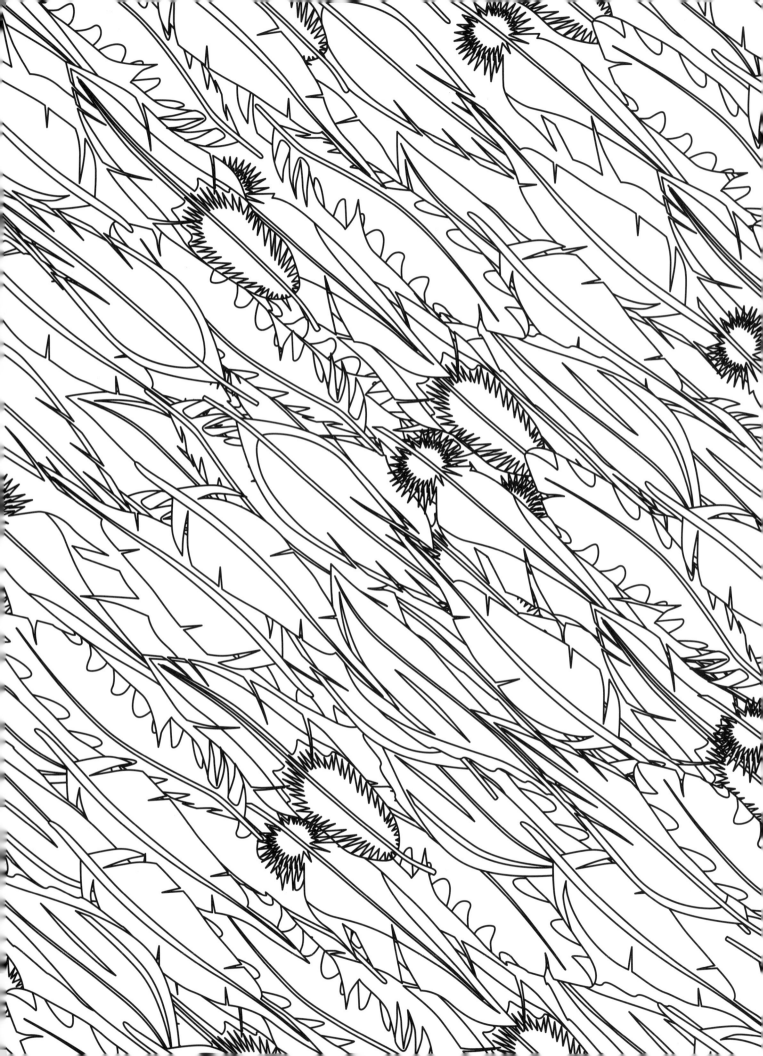

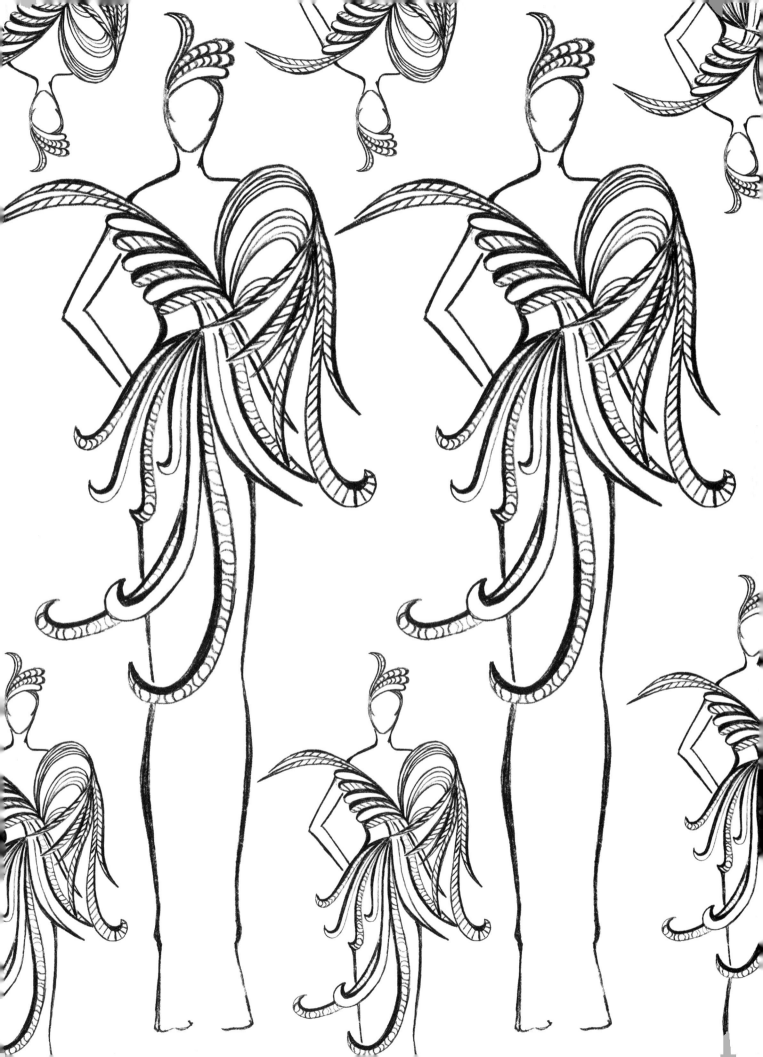

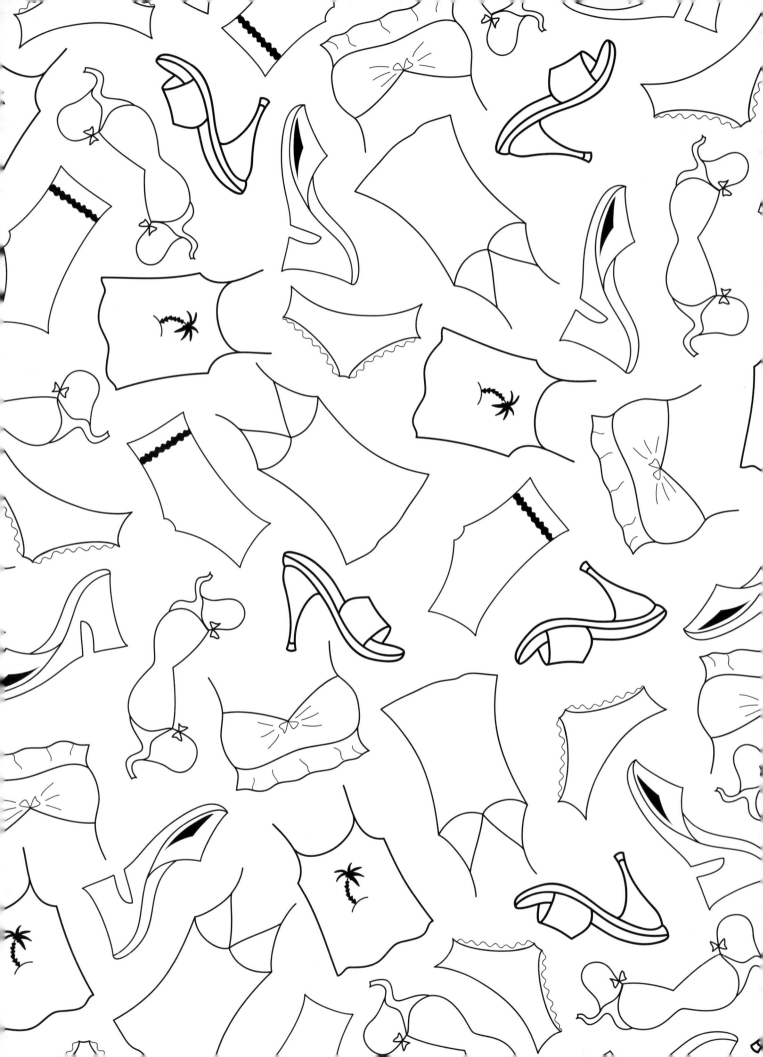

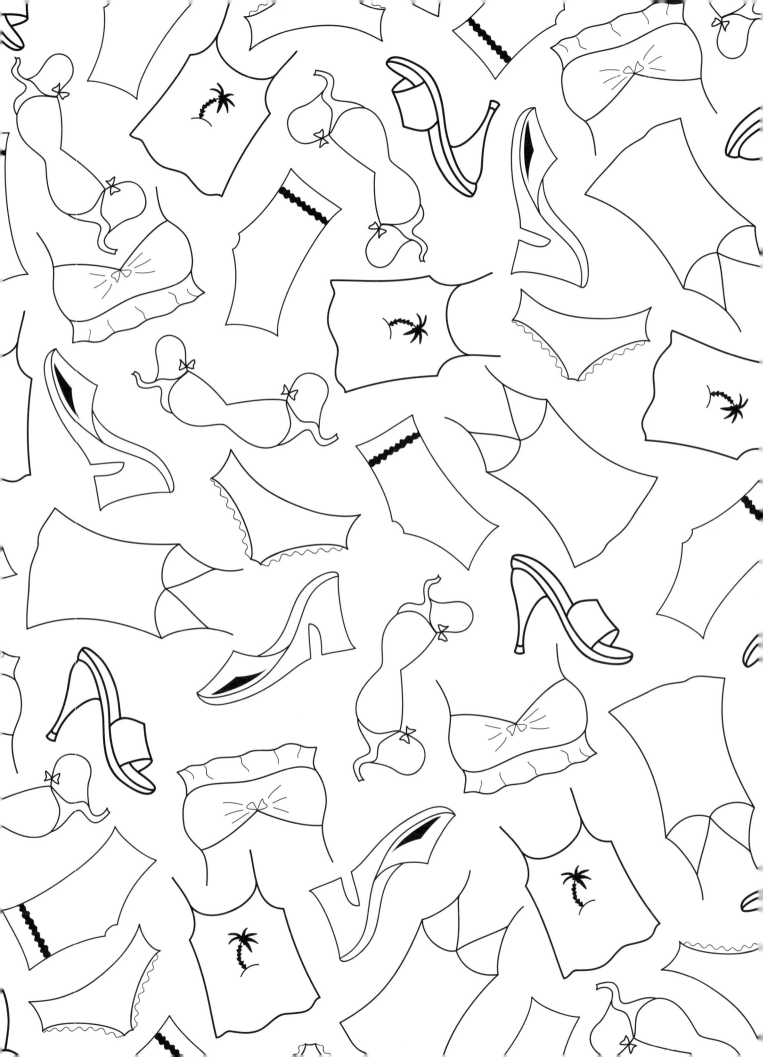

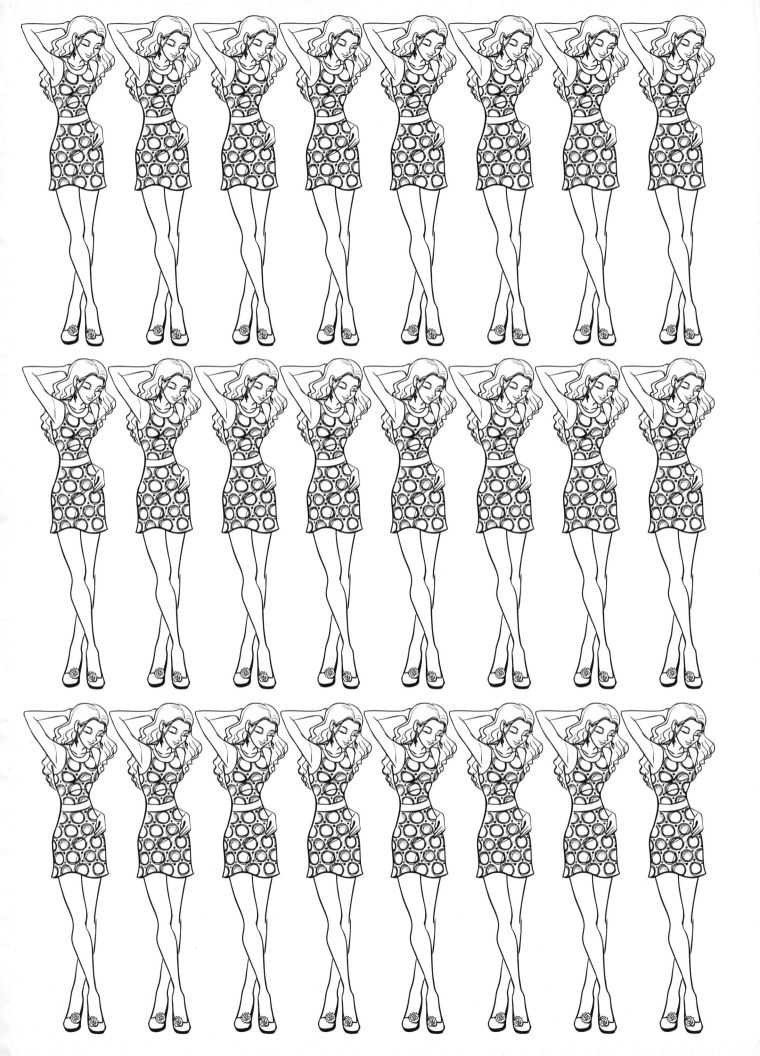

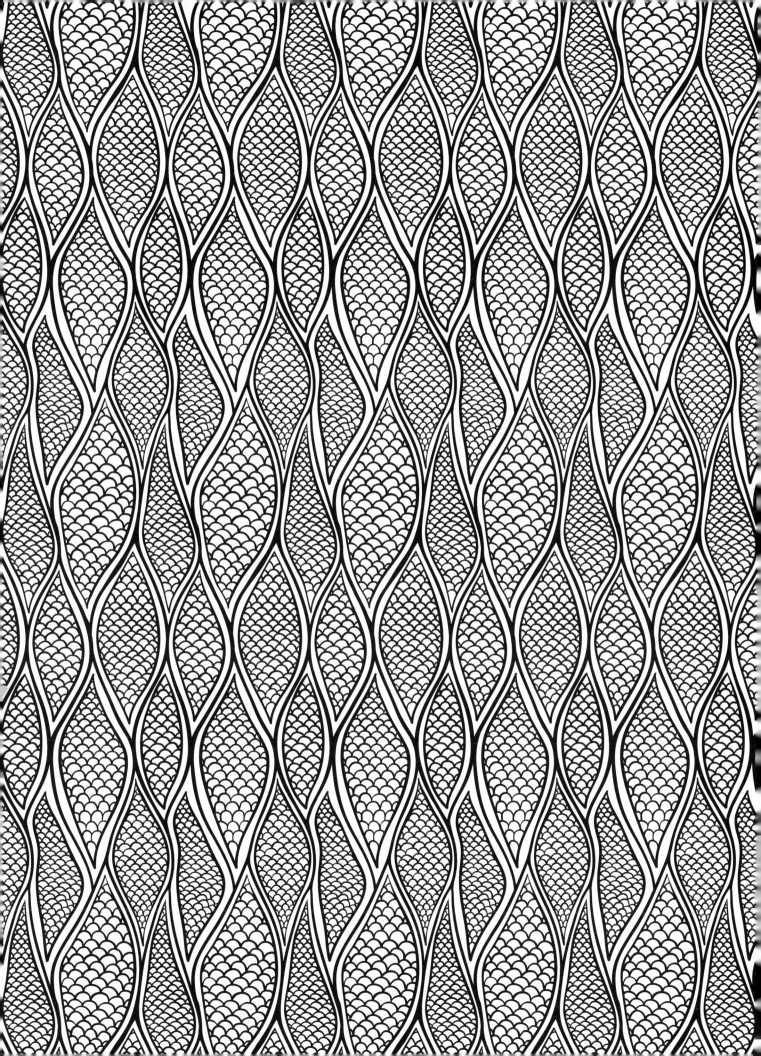

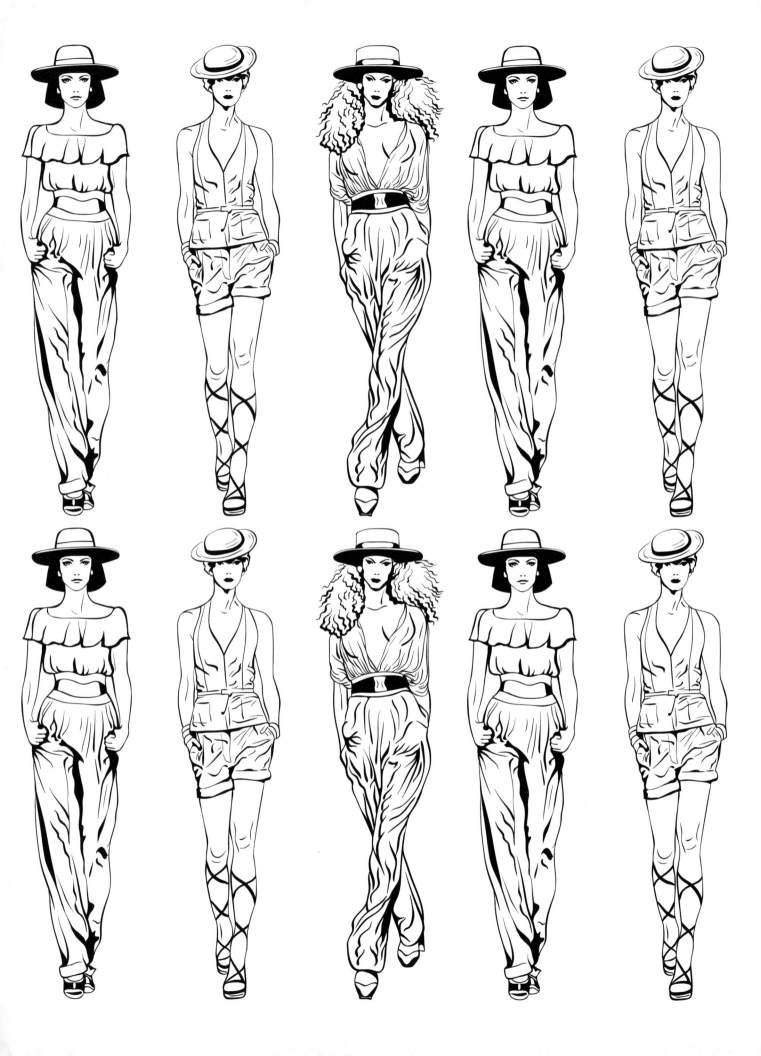

Batten
14/Apr/2016

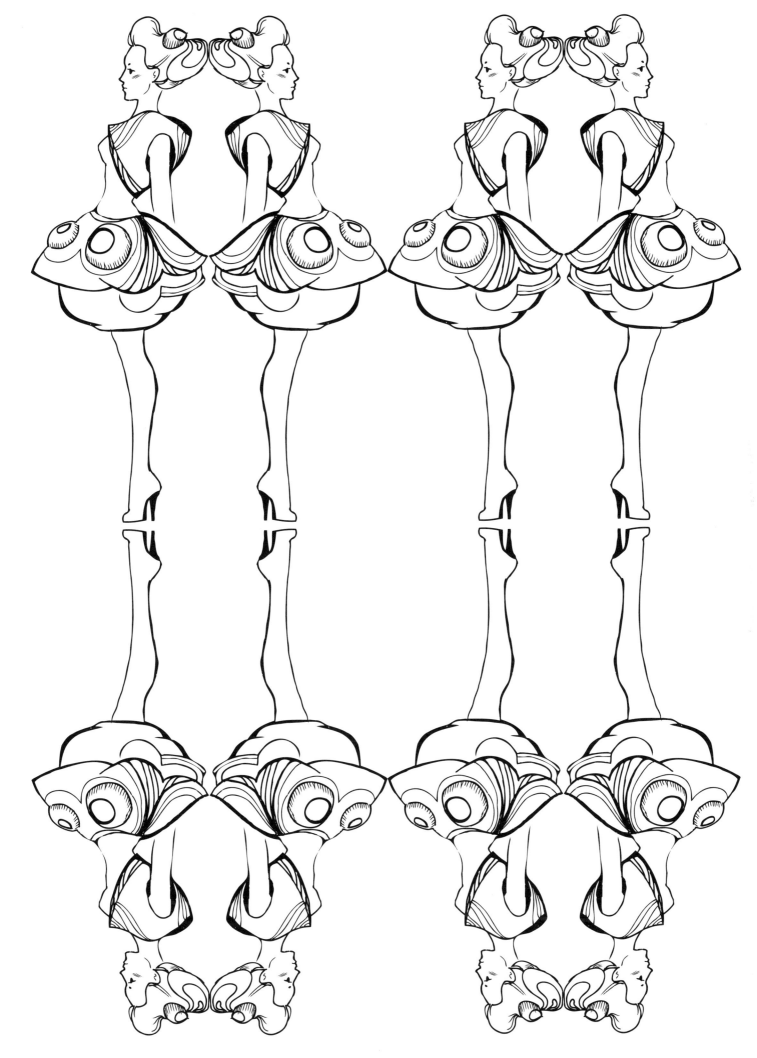

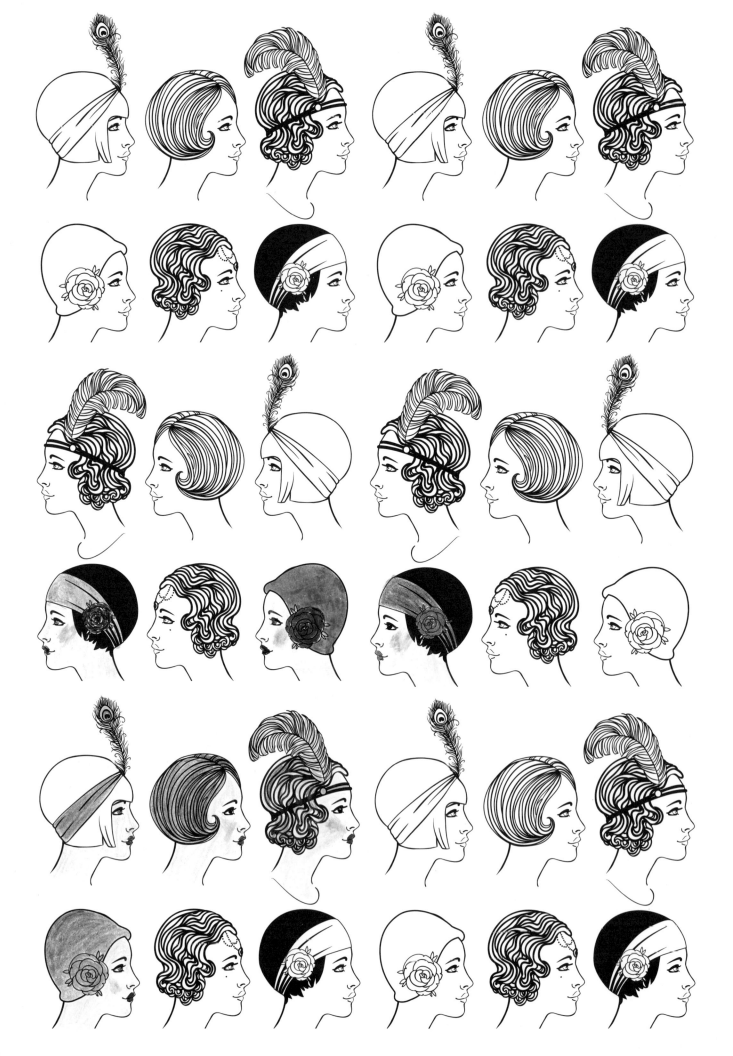

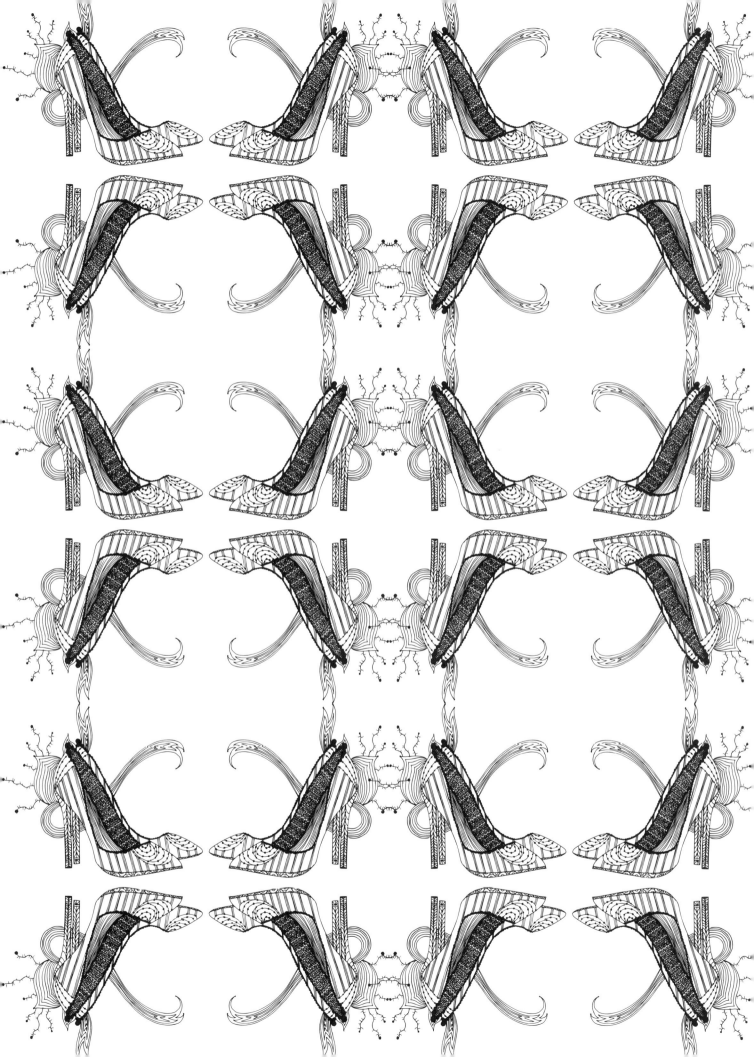

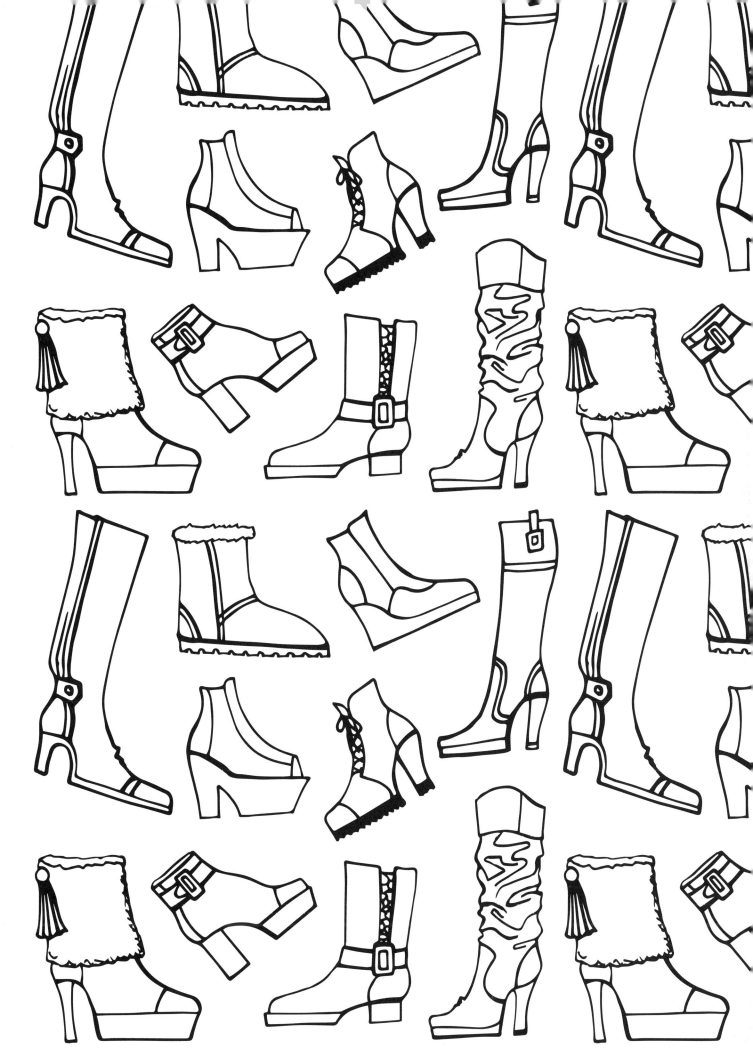

26/May/2016

25/MAY/2016

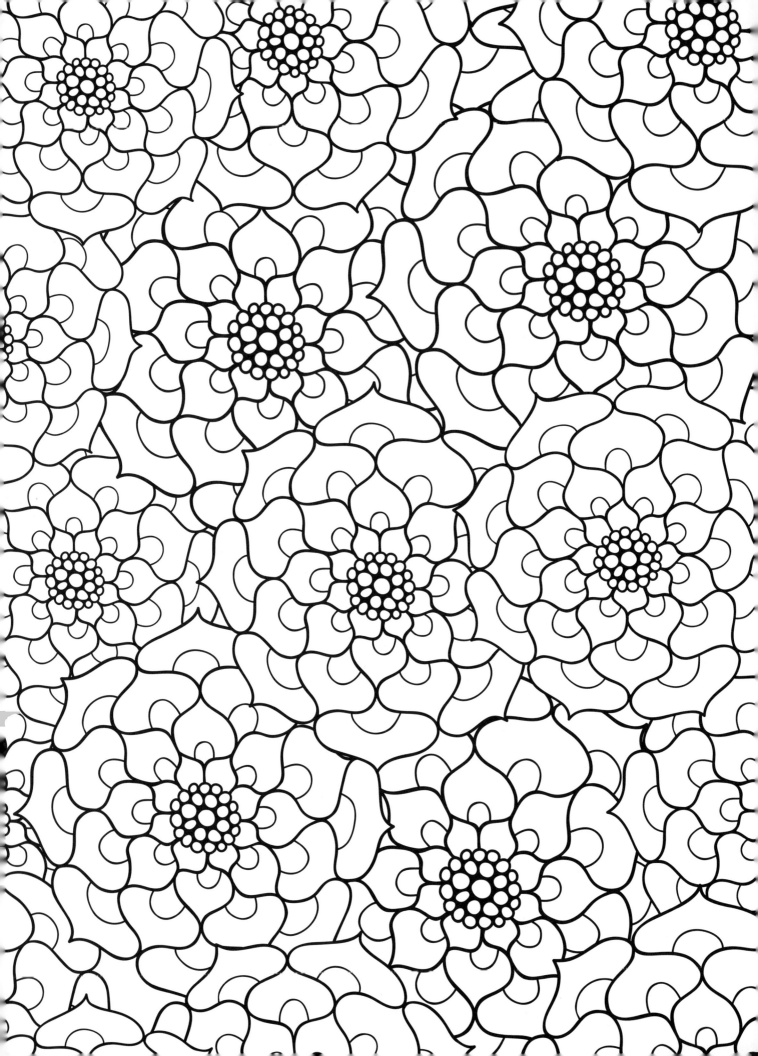

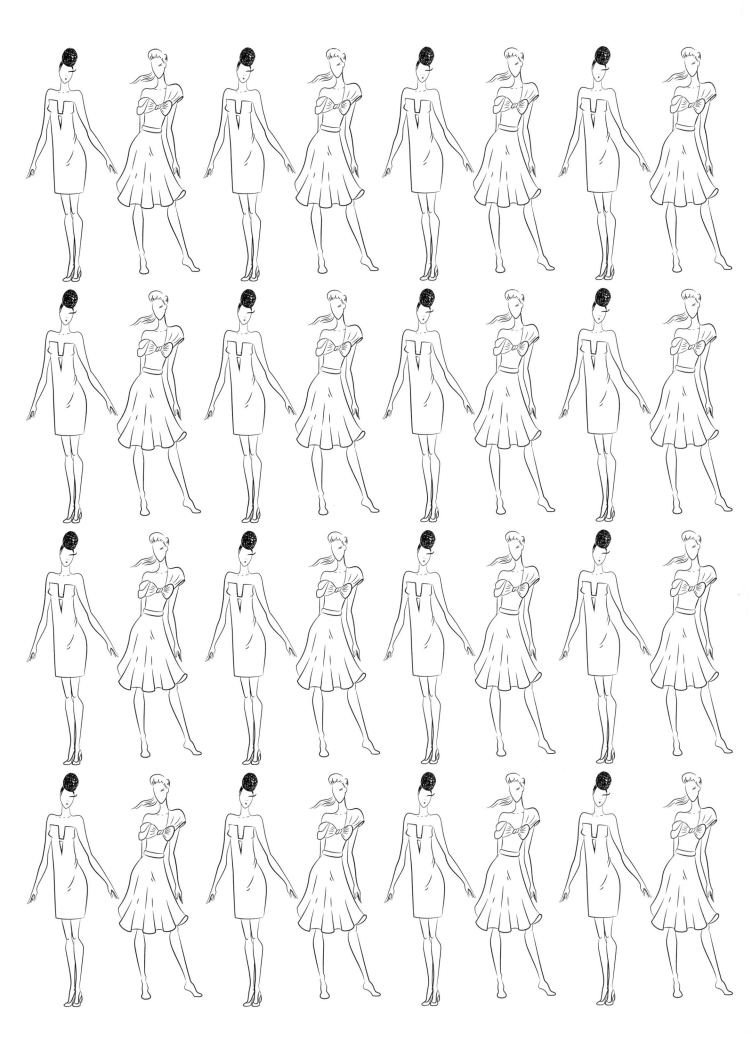

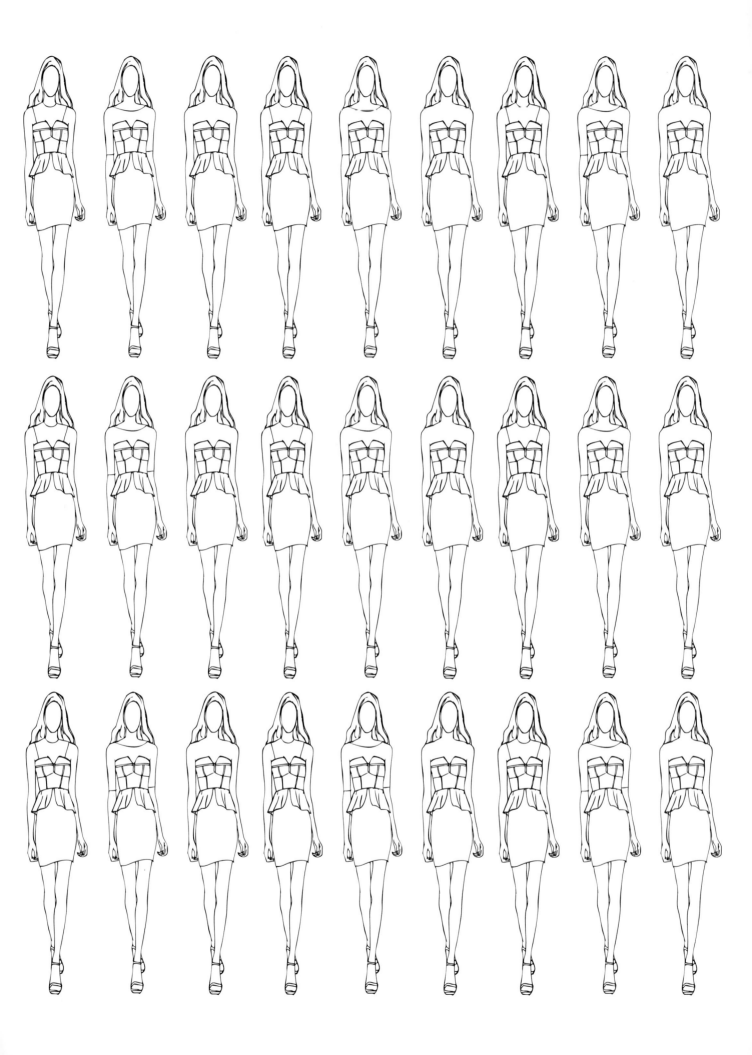

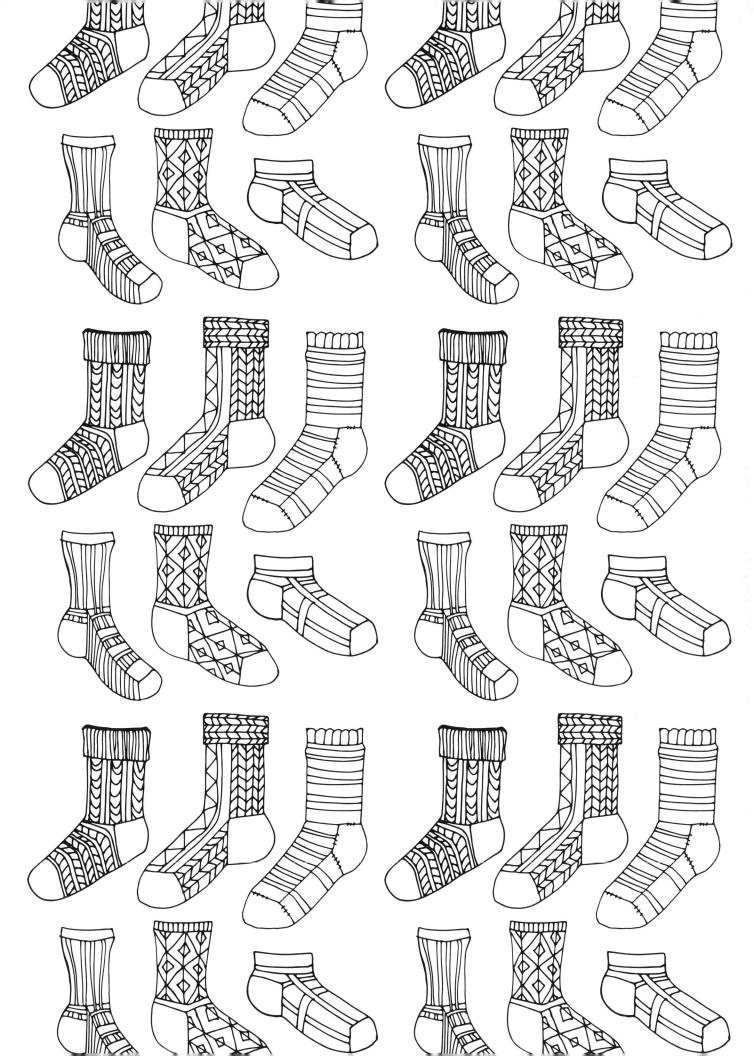

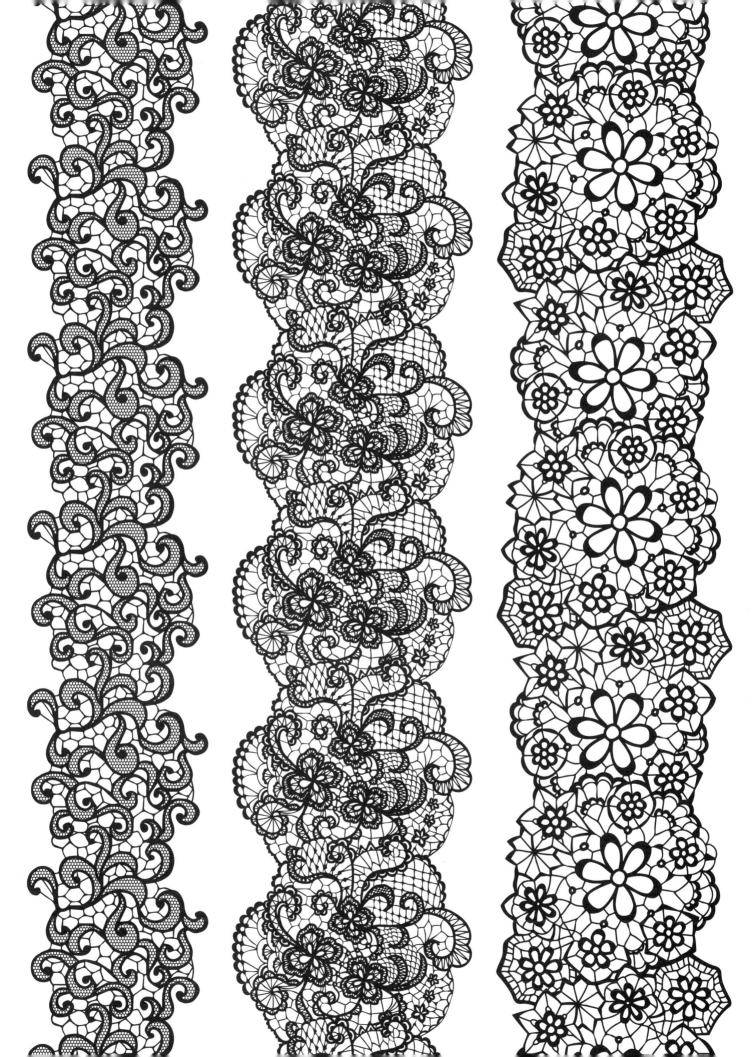

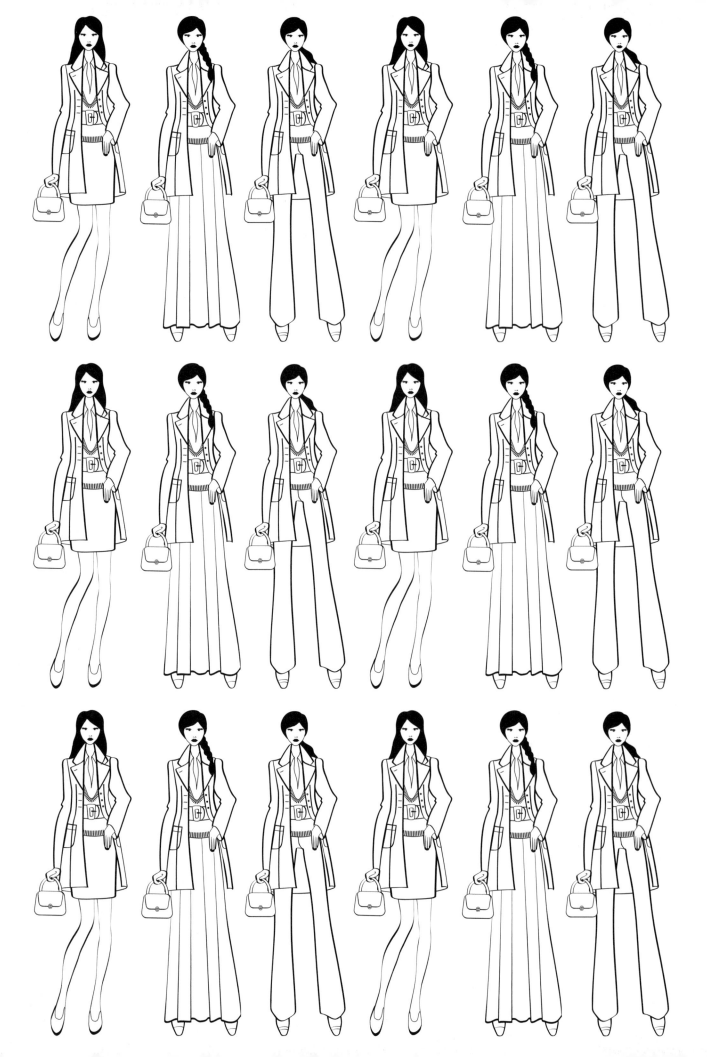

25/MAY/2016

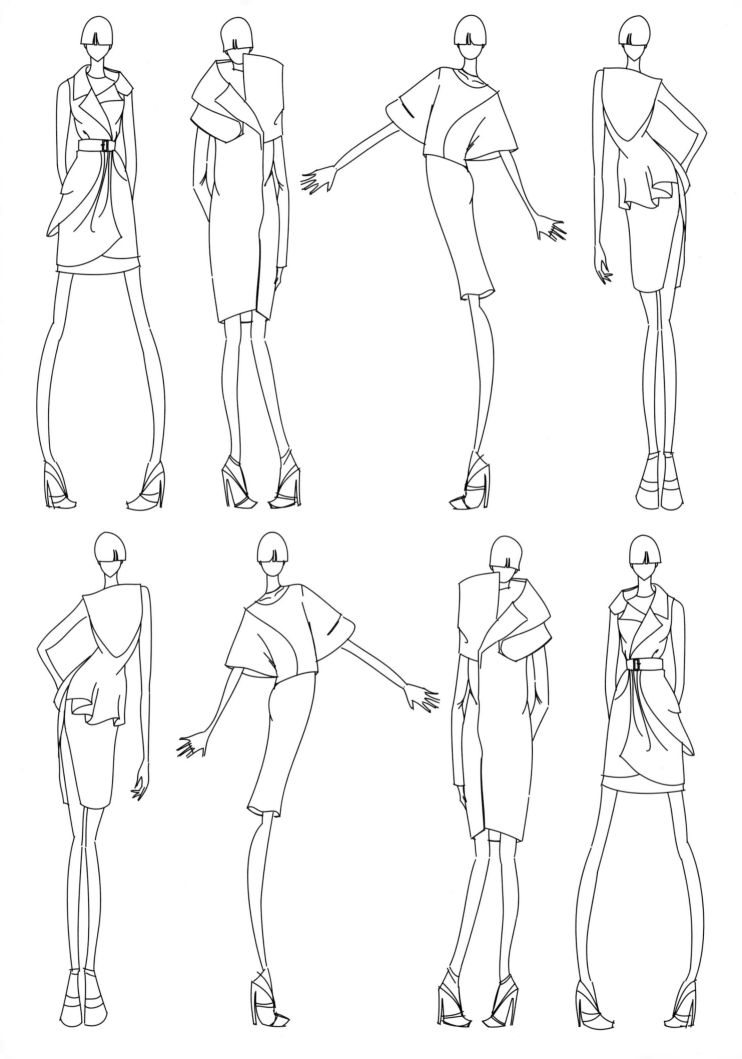

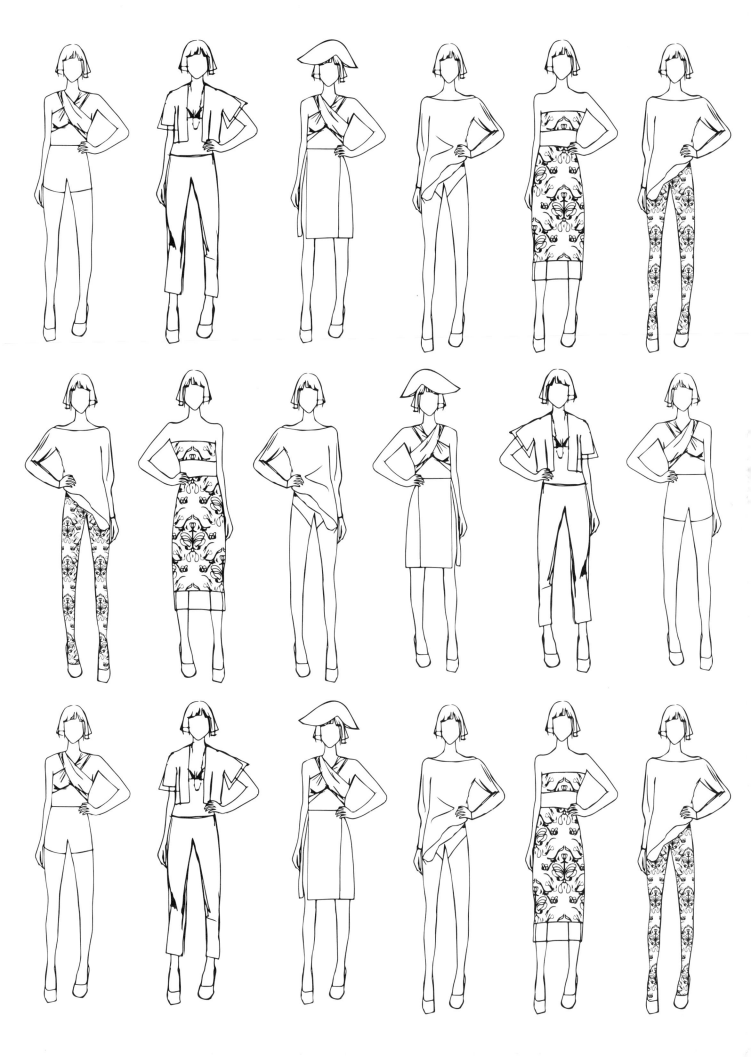

THIS IS A CARLTON BOOK

Published by Carlton Books Ltd
20 Mortimer Street
London W1T 3JW

Copyright © 2016 Carlton Books Ltd

A CIP catalogue record for this book is available from the British Library

10 9 8 7 6 5 4 3 2 1

ISBN 978-1-78177-256-0

Printed in China

Picture credits: Shutterstock.com and Thinkstock.com